The Thinking Tree

# FACES & FEELINGS
## 75 EXERCISES

*Coloring with Connection*
*for Social Comfort &*
*Emotional Processing*

## BRAIN GAMES

Created by Sarah Janisse Brown

The Thinking Tree, LLC – Copyright 2023

FunSchooling.com

By Sarah Janisse Brown
the Creator of
Dyslexia Games Therapy
And Publisher of
Math Craft for Dyscalculia

FunSchooling.com
DyslexiaGames.com

Name:

# HOW TO USE THIS BOOK

This is a coloring book and activity book with fifty photos of faces, shown in grayscale, presented along with a few different thinking activities and logic games.

We present images of people of various races, showing different moods, and include children with disabilities and Down Syndrome. There are animal faces and human faces, all showing different feelings. After every five face pages there will be a "Thinking Page" where the student can freely write about their thoughts. Next is a "Draw Anything Pages" and a "Logic Page". At first it may be hard for the student to use an open ended activity page. Feel free to give the student some prompts or ask them to write about their special interest or recent experiences.

The person using the book should look at the faces and consider how each person or animal is feeling. They will color the eyes in order to become more comfortable with eye contact. If you are a parent, teacher, therapist or friend who is working with a student be open to helping with some of the activities in order to be an example. For example take turns working on each page. Talk about your feelings and the feeling of the person or animal in each picture.

The goal is for the students using the book to become more interested in the faces, feelings and thoughts of others. Some people avoid looking at faces, this behavior causes them to become unaware of how people express feeling through facial expressions. When a child or person of any age becomes comfortable with eye contact they may begin to over come some of their social struggles, and it will be easier to make friends.

Parents: If you are working with a child who needs extra support please feel free to help them with the activities and allow the child to choose what page they want to use first. The child should work on one face per day. Be sure to talk with your child about feelings, use a mirror and try to make the face the person or animals is making in the photo.

The child does not need to complete all three steps on each page at one it. It is good to come back to the same picture and finish it in the future. This helps the faces to become familiar over time.
This concept was been introduced in 2016 as a research experiment, and several neurodivergent children experienced improvements in social comfort and emotional understanding, as a result. The therapy is still experimental. Please leave a review to share your experience with us concerning the use of this book.

This activity book is small. We don't want it to feel intimidating or overwhelming. It's easy to take along wherever you go.

# LOOK AT MY FACE!

What color are my eyes?

Color my eyes.

Trace my face!
I am using a:
_ Black Pen
_ Colored Pencil
_ Marker
_ Gel Pen
_ Crayon
_ #2 Pencil

Write one word to describe me:

## COLOR THE FACES
## THAT SHOW HOW I FEEL:

Draw me

# LOOK AT MY FACE!

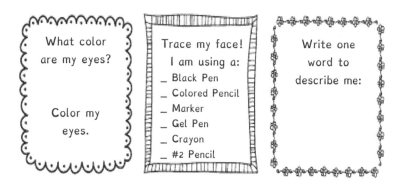

What color are my eyes?

Color my eyes.

Trace my face!
I am using a:
_ Black Pen
_ Colored Pencil
_ Marker
_ Gel Pen
_ Crayon
_ #2 Pencil

Write one word to describe me:

## COLOR THE FACES THAT SHOW HOW I FEEL:

Draw me

# LOOK AT MY FACE!

What color are my eyes?

Color my eyes.

Trace my face!
I am using a:
_ Black Pen
_ Colored Pencil
_ Marker
_ Gel Pen
_ Crayon
_ #2 Pencil

Write one word to describe me:

## COLOR THE FACES
## THAT SHOW HOW I FEEL:

Draw me

# LOOK AT MY FACE!

What color are my eyes?

Color my eyes.

Trace my face!
I am using a:
_ Black Pen
_ Colored Pencil
_ Marker
_ Gel Pen
_ Crayon
_ #2 Pencil

Write one word to describe me:

## COLOR THE FACES THAT SHOW HOW I FEEL:

Draw me

# Today I am thinking about:

_____

_____

_____

_____

_____

_____

_____

_____

_____

_____

_____

_____

_____

_____

_____

_____

_____

_____

_____

_____

_____

_____

# DRAW ANYTHING

# LOGIC GAMES

Draw the missing parts of the pattern or design.

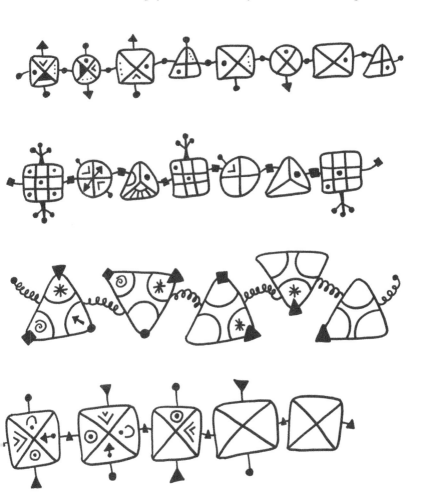

# LOOK AT MY FACE!

What color are my eyes?

Color my eyes.

Trace my face!
I am using a:
_ Black Pen
_ Colored Pencil
_ Marker
_ Gel Pen
_ Crayon
_ #2 Pencil

Write one word to describe me:

## COLOR THE FACES THAT SHOW HOW I FEEL:

Draw me

# LOOK AT MY FACE!

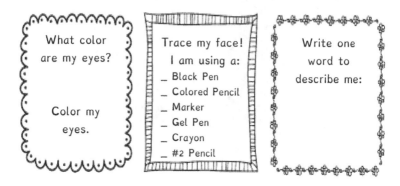

What color are my eyes?

Color my eyes.

Trace my face!
I am using a:
_ Black Pen
_ Colored Pencil
_ Marker
_ Gel Pen
_ Crayon
_ #2 Pencil

Write one word to describe me:

## COLOR THE FACES
## THAT SHOW HOW I FEEL:

Draw me

# LOOK AT MY FACE!

What color are my eyes?

Color my eyes.

Trace my face!
I am using a:
_ Black Pen
_ Colored Pencil
_ Marker
_ Gel Pen
_ Crayon
_ #2 Pencil

Write one word to describe me:

## COLOR THE FACES
## THAT SHOW HOW I FEEL:

Draw me

# LOOK AT MY FACE!

What color are my eyes?

Color my eyes.

Trace my face!
I am using a:
_ Black Pen
_ Colored Pencil
_ Marker
_ Gel Pen
_ Crayon
_ #2 Pencil

Write one word to describe me:

## COLOR THE FACES
## THAT SHOW HOW I FEEL:

Draw me

# LOOK AT MY FACE!

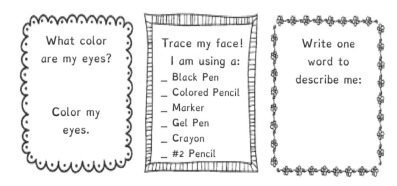

What color are my eyes?

Color my eyes.

Trace my face!
I am using a:
_ Black Pen
_ Colored Pencil
_ Marker
_ Gel Pen
_ Crayon
_ #2 Pencil

Write one word to describe me:

## COLOR THE FACES THAT SHOW HOW I FEEL:

Draw me

# Today I am thinking about:

_____

_____

_____

_____

_____

_____

_____

_____

_____

_____

_____

_____

_____

_____

_____

_____

_____

_____

_____

_____

_____

_____

_____

_____

# DRAW ANYTHING

# LOGIC GAMES

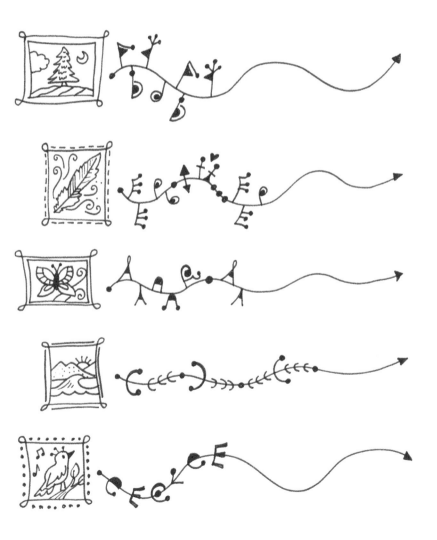

# LOOK AT MY FACE!

What color
are my eyes?

Color my
eyes.

Trace my face!
I am using a:
_ Black Pen
_ Colored Pencil
_ Marker
_ Gel Pen
_ Crayon
_ #2 Pencil

Write one
word to
describe me:

## COLOR THE FACES
## THAT SHOW HOW I FEEL:

Draw me

# LOOK AT MY FACE!

What color are my eyes?

Color my eyes.

Trace my face!
I am using a:
_ Black Pen
_ Colored Pencil
_ Marker
_ Gel Pen
_ Crayon
_ #2 Pencil

Write one word to describe me:

## COLOR THE FACES
## THAT SHOW HOW I FEEL:

Draw me

# LOOK AT MY FACE!

What color are my eyes?

Color my eyes.

Trace my face!

I am using a:
_ Black Pen
_ Colored Pencil
_ Marker
_ Gel Pen
_ Crayon
_ #2 Pencil

Write one word to describe me:

## COLOR THE FACES
## THAT SHOW HOW I FEEL:

Draw me

# LOOK AT MY FACE!

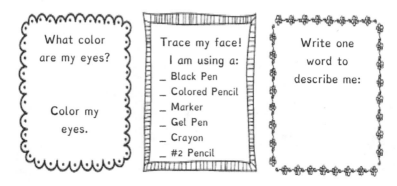

What color are my eyes?

Color my eyes.

Trace my face!
I am using a:
_ Black Pen
_ Colored Pencil
_ Marker
_ Gel Pen
_ Crayon
_ #2 Pencil

Write one word to describe me:

## COLOR THE FACES
## THAT SHOW HOW I FEEL:

Draw me

# LOOK AT MY FACE!

What color are my eyes?

Color my eyes.

Trace my face!
I am using a:
_ Black Pen
_ Colored Pencil
_ Marker
_ Gel Pen
_ Crayon
_ #2 Pencil

Write one word to describe me:

## COLOR THE FACES THAT SHOW HOW I FEEL:

Draw me

# Today I am thinking about:

_____

_____

_____

_____

_____

_____

_____

_____

_____

_____

_____

_____

_____

_____

_____

_____

_____

_____

_____

_____

_____

_____

_____

_____

_____

_____

# DRAW ANYTHING

# LOGIC GAMES

# LOOK AT MY FACE!

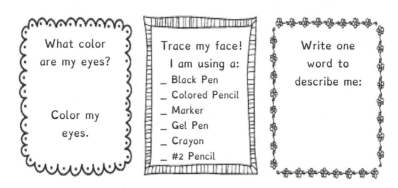

What color are my eyes?

Color my eyes.

Trace my face!
I am using a:
_ Black Pen
_ Colored Pencil
_ Marker
_ Gel Pen
_ Crayon
_ #2 Pencil

Write one word to describe me:

## COLOR THE FACES THAT SHOW HOW I FEEL:

Draw me

# LOOK AT MY FACE!

What color are my eyes?

Color my eyes.

Trace my face!
I am using a:
_ Black Pen
_ Colored Pencil
_ Marker
_ Gel Pen
_ Crayon
_ #2 Pencil

Write one word to describe me:

## COLOR THE FACES
## THAT SHOW HOW I FEEL:

Draw me

# LOOK AT MY FACE!

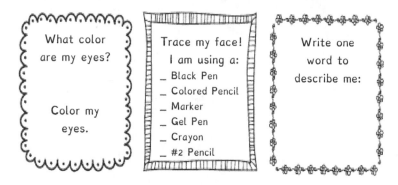

What color are my eyes?

Color my eyes.

Trace my face!
I am using a:
_ Black Pen
_ Colored Pencil
_ Marker
_ Gel Pen
_ Crayon
_ #2 Pencil

Write one word to describe me:

## COLOR THE FACES
## THAT SHOW HOW I FEEL:

Draw me

# LOOK AT MY FACE!

What color are my eyes?

Color my eyes.

Trace my face!
I am using a:
_ Black Pen
_ Colored Pencil
_ Marker
_ Gel Pen
_ Crayon
_ #2 Pencil

Write one word to describe me:

## COLOR THE FACES THAT SHOW HOW I FEEL:

Draw me

# LOOK AT MY FACE!

What color
are my eyes?

Color my
eyes.

Trace my face!
I am using a:
_ Black Pen
_ Colored Pencil
_ Marker
_ Gel Pen
_ Crayon
_ #2 Pencil

Write one
word to
describe me:

## COLOR THE FACES
## THAT SHOW HOW I FEEL:

Draw me

# Today I am thinking about:

_____

_____

_____

_____

_____

_____

_____

_____

_____

_____

_____

_____

_____

_____

_____

_____

_____

_____

_____

_____

_____

_____

_____

_____

_____

# DRAW ANYTHING

# LOGIC GAMES

# LOOK AT MY FACE!

What color
are my eyes?

Color my
eyes.

Trace my face!
I am using a:
_ Black Pen
_ Colored Pencil
_ Marker
_ Gel Pen
_ Crayon
_ #2 Pencil

Write one
word to
describe me:

## COLOR THE FACES
## THAT SHOW HOW I FEEL:

Draw me

# LOOK AT MY FACE!

What color
are my eyes?

Color my
eyes.

Trace my face!
I am using a:
_ Black Pen
_ Colored Pencil
_ Marker
_ Gel Pen
_ Crayon
_ #2 Pencil

Write one
word to
describe me:

## COLOR THE FACES
## THAT SHOW HOW I FEEL:

Draw me

# LOOK AT MY FACE!

What color are my eyes?

Color my eyes.

Trace my face!
I am using a:
_ Black Pen
_ Colored Pencil
_ Marker
_ Gel Pen
_ Crayon
_ #2 Pencil

Write one word to describe me:

## COLOR THE FACES
## THAT SHOW HOW I FEEL:

Draw me

# LOOK AT MY FACE!

What color are my eyes?

Color my eyes.

Trace my face!
I am using a:
_ Black Pen
_ Colored Pencil
_ Marker
_ Gel Pen
_ Crayon
_ #2 Pencil

Write one word to describe me:

## COLOR THE FACES
## THAT SHOW HOW I FEEL:

Draw me

# LOOK AT MY FACE!

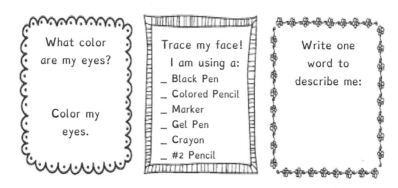

What color are my eyes?

Color my eyes.

Trace my face!
I am using a:
_ Black Pen
_ Colored Pencil
_ Marker
_ Gel Pen
_ Crayon
_ #2 Pencil

Write one word to describe me:

## COLOR THE FACES THAT SHOW HOW I FEEL:

Draw me

# Today I am thinking about:

_____
_____
_____
_____
_____
_____
_____
_____
_____
_____
_____
_____
_____
_____
_____
_____
_____
_____
_____
_____
_____
_____
_____
_____

# DRAW ANYTHING

# LOGIC GAMES

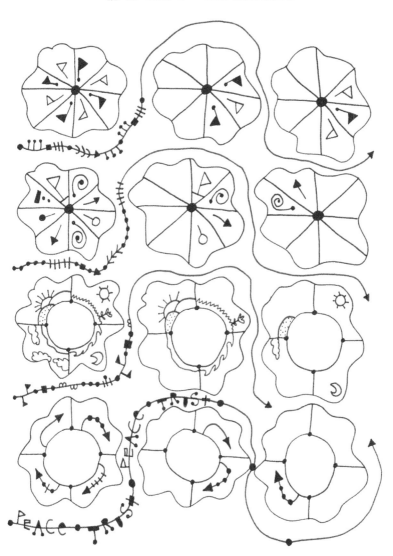

# LOOK AT MY FACE!

What color are my eyes?

Color my eyes.

Trace my face!
I am using a:
_ Black Pen
_ Colored Pencil
_ Marker
_ Gel Pen
_ Crayon
_ #2 Pencil

Write one word to describe me:

## COLOR THE FACES
## THAT SHOW HOW I FEEL:

Draw me

# LOOK AT MY FACE!

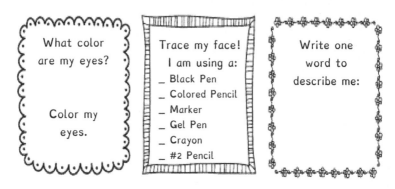

What color
are my eyes?

Color my
eyes.

Trace my face!
I am using a:
_ Black Pen
_ Colored Pencil
_ Marker
_ Gel Pen
_ Crayon
_ #2 Pencil

Write one
word to
describe me:

## COLOR THE FACES
## THAT SHOW HOW I FEEL:

Draw me

# LOOK AT MY FACE!

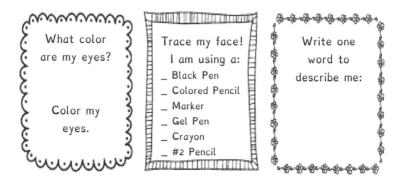

What color
are my eyes?

Color my
eyes.

Trace my face!
I am using a:
_ Black Pen
_ Colored Pencil
_ Marker
_ Gel Pen
_ Crayon
_ #2 Pencil

Write one
word to
describe me:

## COLOR THE FACES
## THAT SHOW HOW I FEEL:

Draw me

# LOOK AT MY FACE!

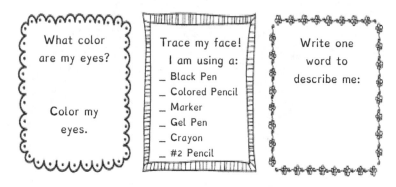

What color are my eyes?

Color my eyes.

Trace my face!
I am using a:
_ Black Pen
_ Colored Pencil
_ Marker
_ Gel Pen
_ Crayon
_ #2 Pencil

Write one word to describe me:

## COLOR THE FACES
## THAT SHOW HOW I FEEL:

Draw me

# LOOK AT MY FACE!

What color are my eyes?

Color my eyes.

Trace my face!
I am using a:
_ Black Pen
_ Colored Pencil
_ Marker
_ Gel Pen
_ Crayon
_ #2 Pencil

Write one word to describe me:

## COLOR THE FACES THAT SHOW HOW I FEEL:

Draw me

# Today I am thinking about:

_____
_____
_____
_____
_____
_____
_____
_____
_____
_____
_____
_____
_____
_____
_____
_____
_____
_____
_____
_____
_____
_____
_____
_____
_____
_____
_____

# DRAW ANYTHING

# LOGIC GAMES

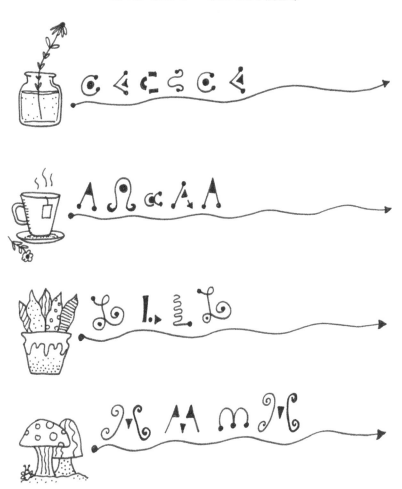

# LOOK AT MY FACE!

What color are my eyes?

Color my eyes.

Trace my face!
I am using a:
_ Black Pen
_ Colored Pencil
_ Marker
_ Gel Pen
_ Crayon
_ #2 Pencil

Write one word to describe me:

## COLOR THE FACES THAT SHOW HOW I FEEL:

Draw me

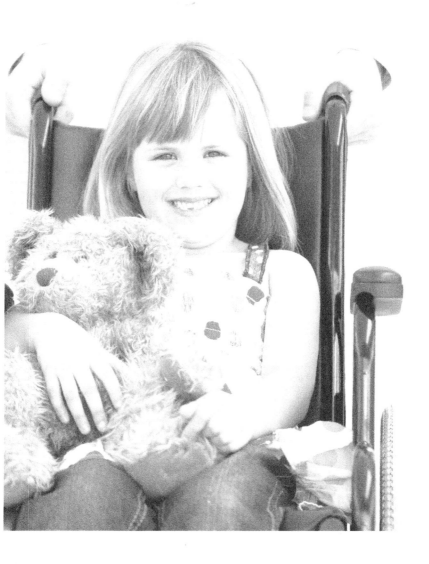

# LOOK AT MY FACE!

What color are my eyes?

Color my eyes.

Trace my face!
I am using a:
_ Black Pen
_ Colored Pencil
_ Marker
_ Gel Pen
_ Crayon
_ #2 Pencil

Write one word to describe me:

## COLOR THE FACES THAT SHOW HOW I FEEL:

Draw me

# LOOK AT MY FACE!

What color are my eyes?

Color my eyes.

Trace my face!
I am using a:
_ Black Pen
_ Colored Pencil
_ Marker
_ Gel Pen
_ Crayon
_ #2 Pencil

Write one word to describe me:

## COLOR THE FACES THAT SHOW HOW I FEEL:

Draw me

# LOOK AT MY FACE!

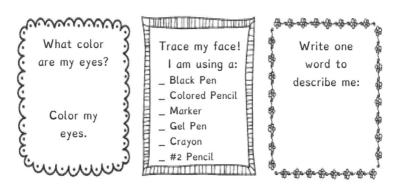

What color
are my eyes?

Color my
eyes.

Trace my face!
I am using a:
_ Black Pen
_ Colored Pencil
_ Marker
_ Gel Pen
_ Crayon
_ #2 Pencil

Write one
word to
describe me:

## COLOR THE FACES
## THAT SHOW HOW I FEEL:

Draw me

# Today I am thinking about:

_____
_____
_____
_____
_____
_____
_____
_____
_____
_____
_____
_____
_____
_____
_____
_____
_____
_____
_____
_____
_____
_____
_____
_____

# DRAW ANYTHING

# LOGIC GAMES

# LOOK AT MY FACE!

What color are my eyes?

Color my eyes.

Trace my face!
I am using a:
_ Black Pen
_ Colored Pencil
_ Marker
_ Gel Pen
_ Crayon
_ #2 Pencil

Write one word to describe me:

## COLOR THE FACES THAT SHOW HOW I FEEL:

Draw me

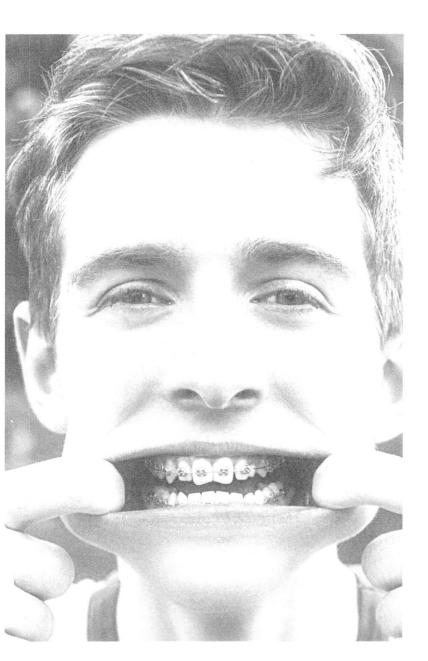

# LOOK AT MY FACE!

What color are my eyes?

Color my eyes.

Trace my face!
I am using a:
_ Black Pen
_ Colored Pencil
_ Marker
_ Gel Pen
_ Crayon
_ #2 Pencil

Write one word to describe me:

## COLOR THE FACES THAT SHOW HOW I FEEL:

Draw me

# LOOK AT MY FACE!

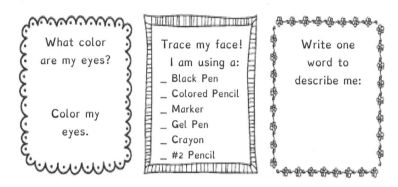

What color are my eyes?

Color my eyes.

Trace my face!
I am using a:
_ Black Pen
_ Colored Pencil
_ Marker
_ Gel Pen
_ Crayon
_ #2 Pencil

Write one word to describe me:

## COLOR THE FACES
## THAT SHOW HOW I FEEL:

Draw me

# LOOK AT MY FACE!

What color
are my eyes?

Color my
eyes.

Trace my face!
I am using a:
_ Black Pen
_ Colored Pencil
_ Marker
_ Gel Pen
_ Crayon
_ #2 Pencil

Write one
word to
describe me:

## COLOR THE FACES
## THAT SHOW HOW I FEEL:

Draw me

# LOOK AT MY FACE!

What color are my eyes?

Color my eyes.

Trace my face!
I am using a:
_ Black Pen
_ Colored Pencil
_ Marker
_ Gel Pen
_ Crayon
_ #2 Pencil

Write one word to describe me:

## COLOR THE FACES THAT SHOW HOW I FEEL:

Draw me

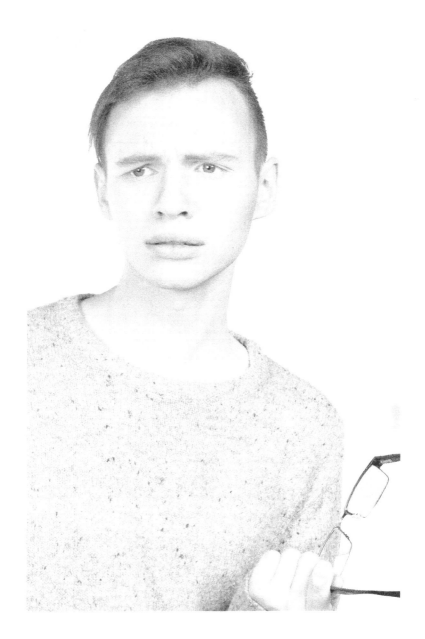

# Today I am thinking about:

_____
_____
_____
_____
_____
_____
_____
_____
_____
_____
_____
_____
_____
_____
_____
_____
_____
_____
_____
_____
_____
_____
_____
_____

# DRAW ANYTHING

# LOGIC GAMES

# LOOK AT MY FACE!

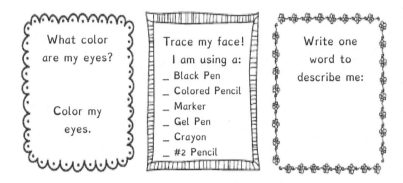

What color are my eyes?

Color my eyes.

Trace my face!
I am using a:
_ Black Pen
_ Colored Pencil
_ Marker
_ Gel Pen
_ Crayon
_ #2 Pencil

Write one word to describe me:

## COLOR THE FACES THAT SHOW HOW I FEEL:

Draw me

# LOOK AT MY FACE!

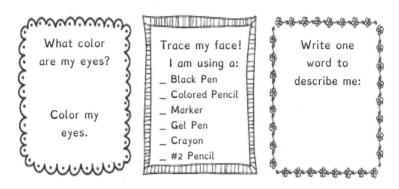

What color are my eyes?

Color my eyes.

Trace my face!
I am using a:
_ Black Pen
_ Colored Pencil
_ Marker
_ Gel Pen
_ Crayon
_ #2 Pencil

Write one word to describe me:

## COLOR THE FACES THAT SHOW HOW I FEEL:

Draw me

# LOOK AT MY FACE!

What color
are my eyes?

Color my
eyes.

Trace my face!
I am using a:
_ Black Pen
_ Colored Pencil
_ Marker
_ Gel Pen
_ Crayon
_ #2 Pencil

Write one
word to
describe me:

## COLOR THE FACES
## THAT SHOW HOW I FEEL:

Draw me

# LOOK AT MY FACE!

What color are my eyes?

Color my eyes.

Trace my face!
I am using a:
_ Black Pen
_ Colored Pencil
_ Marker
_ Gel Pen
_ Crayon
_ #2 Pencil

Write one word to describe me:

## COLOR THE FACES THAT SHOW HOW I FEEL:

Draw me

# LOOK AT MY FACE!

What color
are my eyes?

Color my
eyes.

Trace my face!
I am using a:
_ Black Pen
_ Colored Pencil
_ Marker
_ Gel Pen
_ Crayon
_ #2 Pencil

Write one
word to
describe me:

## COLOR THE FACES
## THAT SHOW HOW I FEEL:

Draw me

# Today I am thinking about:

# DRAW ANYTHING

# LOGIC GAMES

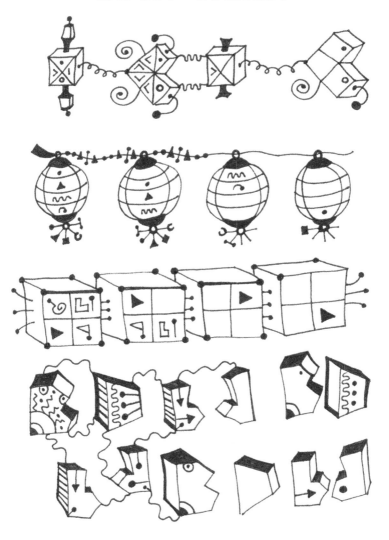

# LOOK AT MY FACE!

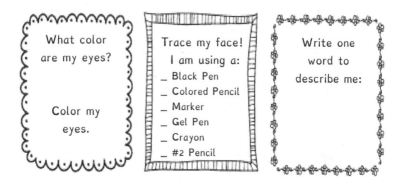

What color
are my eyes?

Color my
eyes.

Trace my face!
I am using a:
_ Black Pen
_ Colored Pencil
_ Marker
_ Gel Pen
_ Crayon
_ #2 Pencil

Write one
word to
describe me:

## COLOR THE FACES
## THAT SHOW HOW I FEEL:

Draw me

# LOOK AT MY FACE!

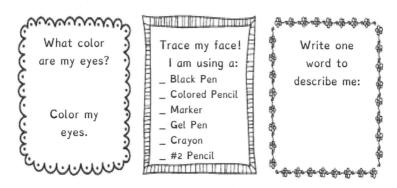

What color are my eyes?

Color my eyes.

Trace my face!
I am using a:
_ Black Pen
_ Colored Pencil
_ Marker
_ Gel Pen
_ Crayon
_ #2 Pencil

Write one word to describe me:

## COLOR THE FACES THAT SHOW HOW I FEEL:

Draw me

# LOOK AT MY FACE!

What color are my eyes?

Color my eyes.

Trace my face!
I am using a:
_ Black Pen
_ Colored Pencil
_ Marker
_ Gel Pen
_ Crayon
_ #2 Pencil

Write one word to describe me:

## COLOR THE FACES
## THAT SHOW HOW I FEEL:

Draw me

# LOOK AT MY FACE!

What color are my eyes?

Color my eyes.

Trace my face!
I am using a:
_ Black Pen
_ Colored Pencil
_ Marker
_ Gel Pen
_ Crayon
_ #2 Pencil

Write one word to describe me:

## COLOR THE FACES THAT SHOW HOW I FEEL:

Draw me

# LOOK AT MY FACE!

What color are my eyes?

Color my eyes.

Trace my face!
I am using a:
_ Black Pen
_ Colored Pencil
_ Marker
_ Gel Pen
_ Crayon
_ #2 Pencil

Write one word to describe me:

## COLOR THE FACES
## THAT SHOW HOW I FEEL:

Draw me

# Today I am thinking about:

_____

_____

_____

_____

_____

_____

_____

_____

_____

_____

_____

_____

_____

_____

_____

_____

_____

_____

_____

_____

_____

_____

_____

_____

_____

# DRAW ANYTHING

# LOGIC GAMES

# LOOK AT MY FACE!

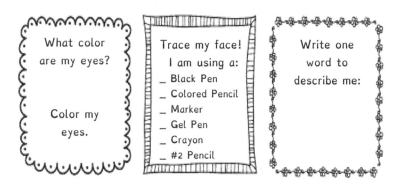

What color are my eyes?

Color my eyes.

Trace my face!
I am using a:
_ Black Pen
_ Colored Pencil
_ Marker
_ Gel Pen
_ Crayon
_ #2 Pencil

Write one word to describe me:

## COLOR THE FACES THAT SHOW HOW I FEEL:

Draw me

# LOOK AT MY FACE!

What color are my eyes?

Color my eyes.

Trace my face!
I am using a:
_ Black Pen
_ Colored Pencil
_ Marker
_ Gel Pen
_ Crayon
_ #2 Pencil

Write one word to describe me:

## COLOR THE FACES
## THAT SHOW HOW I FEEL:

Draw me

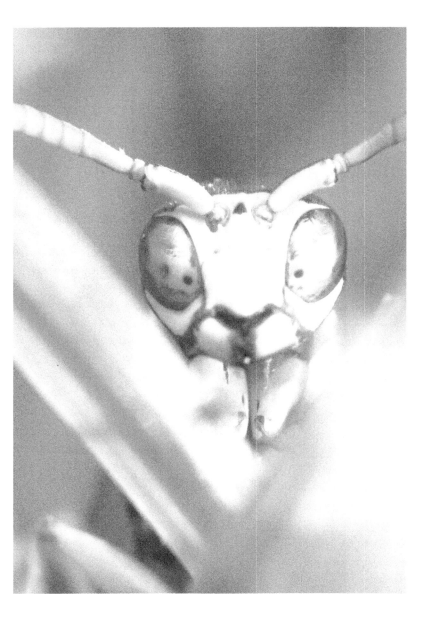

# LOOK AT MY FACE!

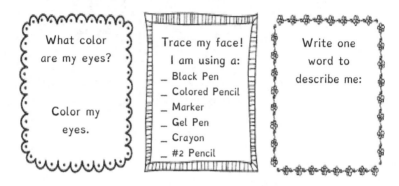

What color are my eyes?

Color my eyes.

Trace my face!
I am using a:
_ Black Pen
_ Colored Pencil
_ Marker
_ Gel Pen
_ Crayon
_ #2 Pencil

Write one word to describe me:

## COLOR THE FACES
## THAT SHOW HOW I FEEL:

Draw me

# LOOK AT MY FACE!

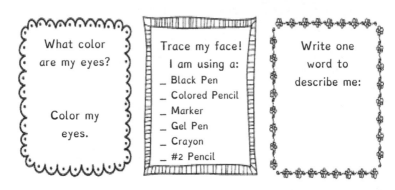

What color are my eyes?

Color my eyes.

Trace my face!
I am using a:
_ Black Pen
_ Colored Pencil
_ Marker
_ Gel Pen
_ Crayon
_ #2 Pencil

Write one word to describe me:

## COLOR THE FACES THAT SHOW HOW I FEEL:

Draw me

# LOOK AT MY FACE!

What color are my eyes?

Color my eyes.

Trace my face!
I am using a:
_ Black Pen
_ Colored Pencil
_ Marker
_ Gel Pen
_ Crayon
_ #2 Pencil

Write one word to describe me:

## COLOR THE FACES
## THAT SHOW HOW I FEEL:

Draw me

# Today I am thinking about:

_____
_____
_____
_____
_____
_____
_____
_____
_____
_____
_____
_____
_____
_____
_____
_____
_____
_____
_____
_____
_____
_____
_____
_____
_____
_____
_____

# DRAW ANYTHING

# LOGIC GAMES

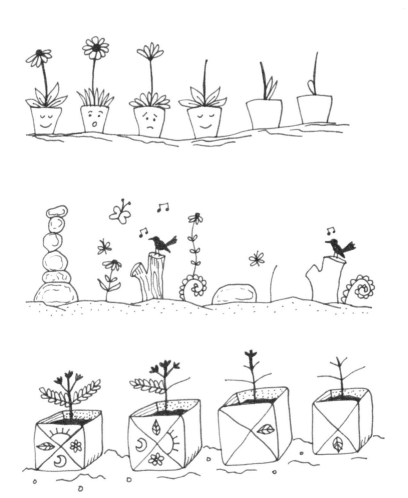

Made in the USA
Coppell, TX
13 February 2023

12739854R00089